Notes from the Universe
Colouring Book

Mike Dooley

HAY HOUSE

Carlsbad, California • New York City • London • Sydney
Johannesburg • Vancouver • Hong Kong • New Delhi

First published and distributed in the United Kingdom by:
Hay House UK Ltd, Astley House, 33 Notting Hill Gate, London W11 3JQ
Tel: +44 (0)20 3675 2450; Fax: +44 (0)20 3675 2451; www.hayhouse.co.uk

Published and distributed in the United States of America by:
Hay House Inc., PO Box 5100, Carlsbad, CA 92018-5100
Tel: (1) 760 431 7695 or (800) 654 5126
Fax: (1) 760 431 6948 or (800) 650 5115; www.hayhouse.com

Published and distributed in Australia by:
Hay House Australia Ltd, 18/36 Ralph St, Alexandria NSW 2015
Tel: (61) 2 9669 4299; Fax: (61) 2 9669 4144; www.hayhouse.com.au

Published and distributed in the Republic of South Africa by:
Hay House SA (Pty) Ltd, PO Box 990, Witkoppen 2068
info@hayhouse.co.za; www.hayhouse.co.za

Published and distributed in India by:
Hay House Publishers India, Muskaan Complex, Plot No.3, B-2,
Vasant Kunj, New Delhi 110 070
Tel: (91) 11 4176 1620; Fax: (91) 11 4176 1630; www.hayhouse.co.in

Distributed in Canada by:
Raincoast Books, 2440 Viking Way, Richmond, B.C. V6V 1N2
Tel: (1) 604 448 7100; Fax: (1) 604 270 7161; www.raincoast.com

A catalogue record for this book is available from the British Library.

ISBN: 978-1-78180-646-3

A Note from Mike

I wrote the first 'Note from the Universe' 15 years ago because it was exactly what I most wanted to receive at the time – inspiration and reassurance from a source greater than myself. The Note was a hit. I was inspired and reassured, and subscribers wanted more. Looking back, I think the demonstration of writing as the Universe, as much as receiving an email from the Universe as subscribers do, helps to create a space that allows us to feel cherished, essential and guided.

On the pages within, we've chosen some of the all-time most popular and empowering Notes ever written and paired them with original, hand-drawn designs that beg to come alive with your own creative sharing. These images are now holding the space for you to revel in the truth of your magnificence and oneness with Source. As you lift pen or pencil, crayon or charcoal, paintbrush or markers to channel your higher-self, trust that you will receive exactly what you most need.

Happy colouring! Happy inspiration! Happy everything!

About Mike

Mike Dooley is a former PriceWaterhouseCoopers international tax consultant turned entrepreneur, and founder of a philosophical Adventurers Club on the Internet that's now home to over 700,000 members from over 182 countries. His inspirational books emphasizing spiritual accountability have been published in 25 languages and he was one of the featured teachers in the international phenomenon, *The Secret*. Today Mike may be best known for his free Notes from the Universe e-mailings, social network postings and his *New York Times* bestsellers *Infinite Possibilities* and *Leveraging the Universe*. Mike lives what he teaches, travelling internationally speaking on life, dreams and happiness.

Find out more at **tut.com**

About Gina

Gina is a new addition to Mike's team at TUT's Adventurers Club, contributing her dual talents as both a graphic designer and front-end web developer.

Before relocating to Orlando, Florida, Gina was raised in Indianapolis, Indiana, where she earned her BS in Media Arts and Science, developed a love for local artistry and began cultivating her skills as a visual artist. She gains inspiration from family, music, travelling and the culinary world.

www.ginairie.com

PERSPECTIVE CHANGES EVERYTHING

Tell me, when you think of taking consistent action in the general direction of your dreams, do you imagine discipline, stamina, work, sacrifice, monotony, courage and strategies? Or do you imagine adventure, discovery, new friends, excitement at the crack of dawn, magic, surprises, fun, laughter and, on occasion, the Macarena?

Cool! Me too, 'HEY!'

The Universe

Your chosen perspective changes everything.

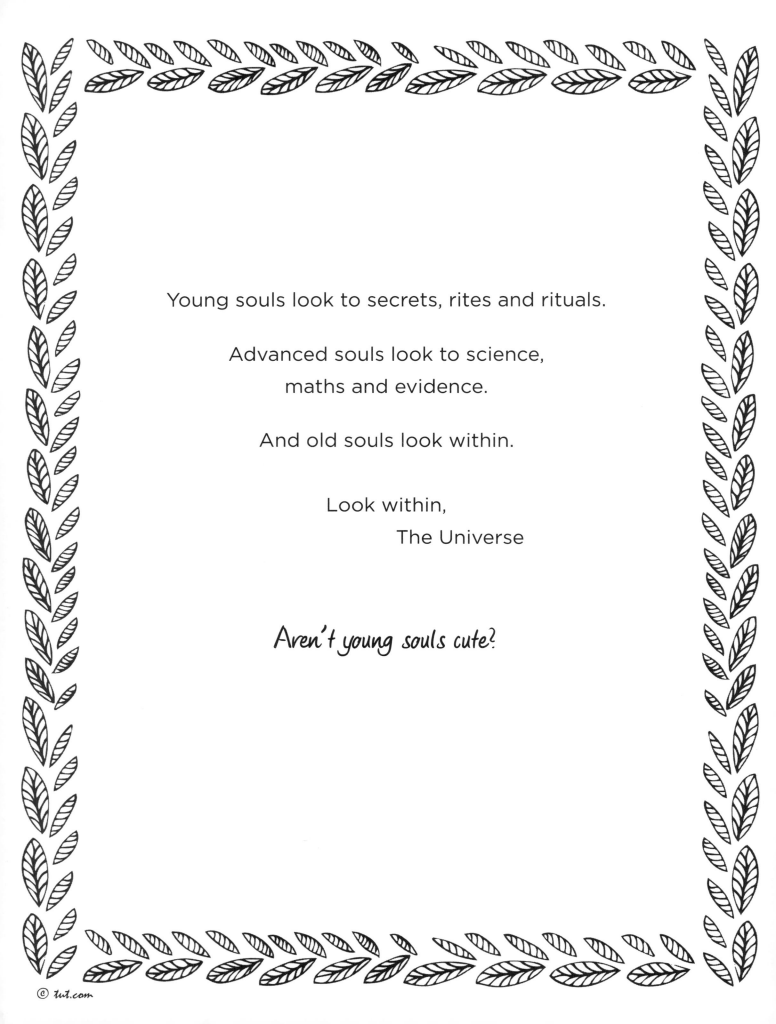

Young souls look to secrets, rites and rituals.

Advanced souls look to science,
maths and evidence.

And old souls look within.

Look within,
        The Universe

Aren't young souls cute?

All you want LIES within you

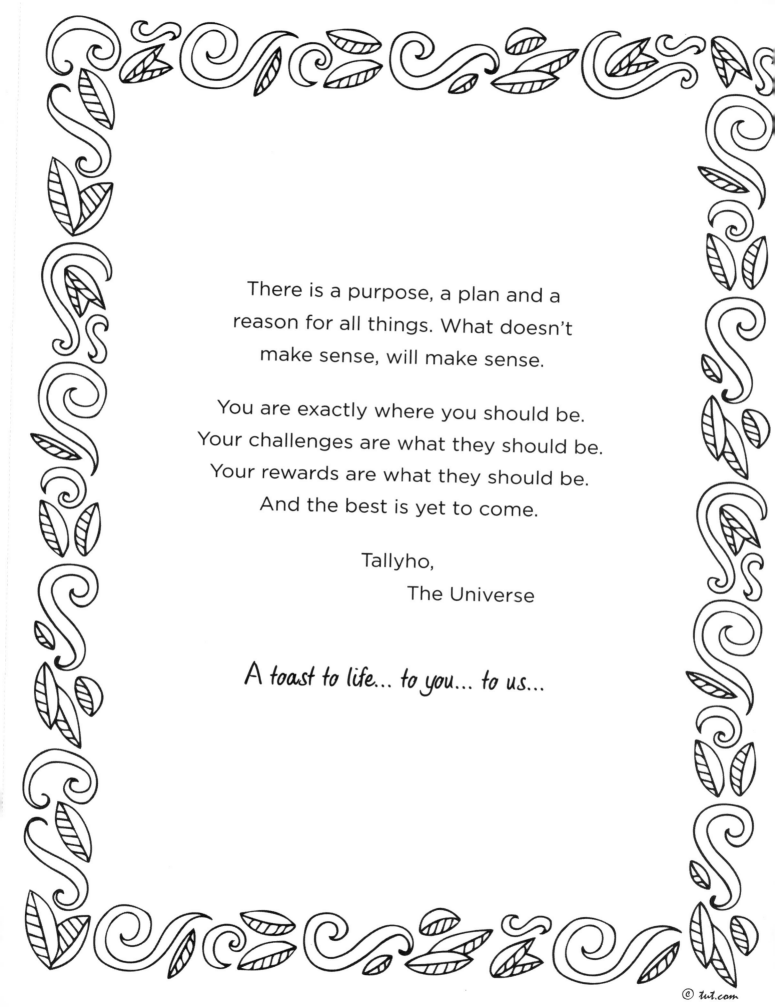

There is a purpose, a plan and a
reason for all things. What doesn't
make sense, will make sense.

You are exactly where you should be.
Your challenges are what they should be.
Your rewards are what they should be.
And the best is yet to come.

Tallyho,
    The Universe

A toast to life... to you... to us...

Always trust your dreams.

They've chosen you as much
as you've chosen them.

Tallyho,
The Universe

And it really ticked-off all the other dreams, too.

There are those who absolutely think all the right thoughts. Yet if they're not doing all they can, with what they've got, from where they are, then you can just guess what else they're probably thinking.

And those other thoughts are busy at work, too.

Tallyho,
    The Universe

Start, stretch, reach, climb, go.
Because just waiting for the magic...
takes forever.

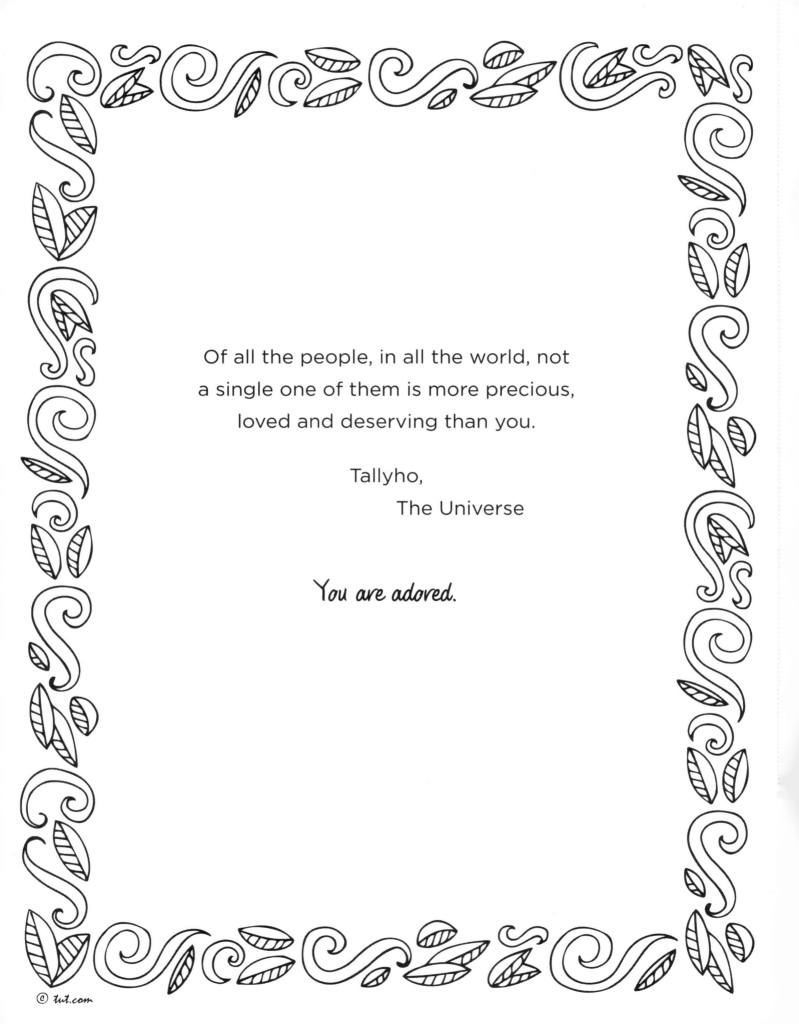

Of all the people, in all the world, not
a single one of them is more precious,
loved and deserving than you.

Tallyho,
The Universe

You are adored.

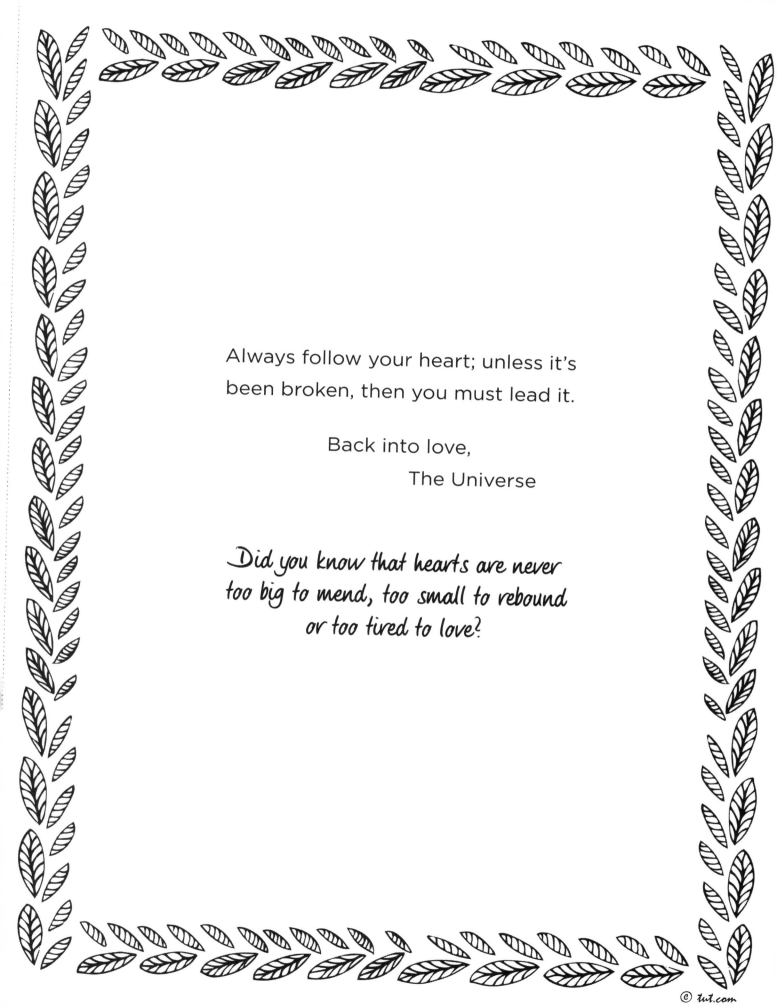

Always follow your heart; unless it's been broken, then you must lead it.

Back into love,
        The Universe

Did you know that hearts are never too big to mend, too small to rebound or too tired to love?

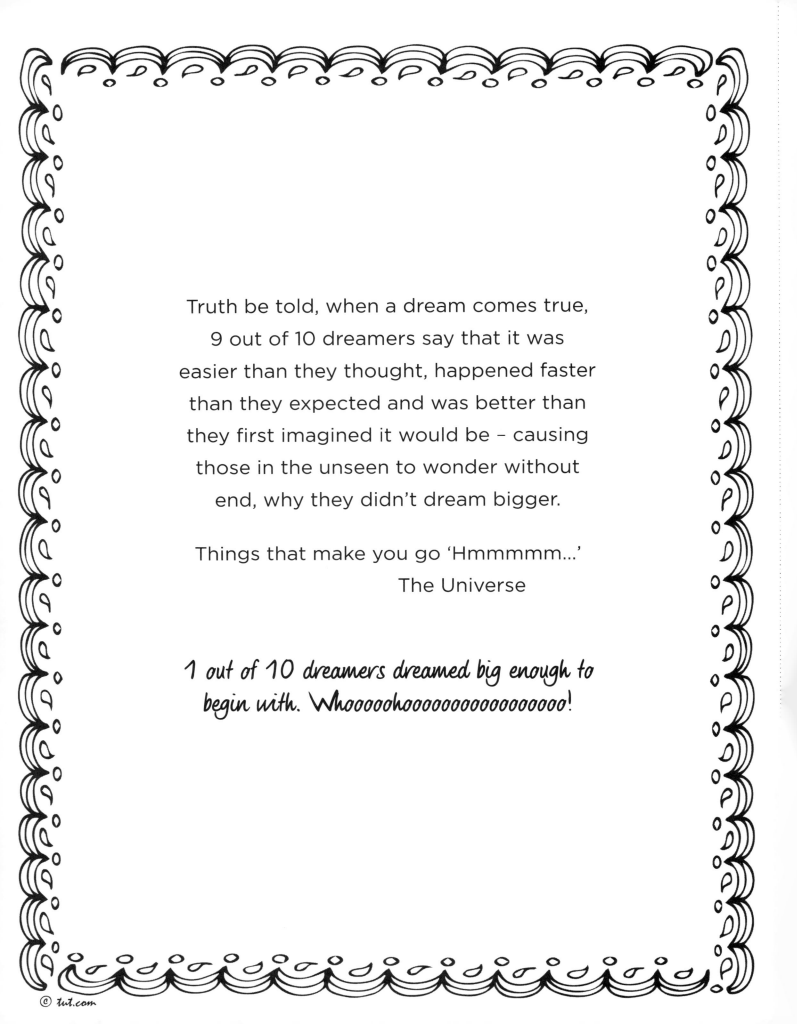

Truth be told, when a dream comes true,
9 out of 10 dreamers say that it was
easier than they thought, happened faster
than they expected and was better than
they first imagined it would be – causing
those in the unseen to wonder without
end, why they didn't dream bigger.

Things that make you go 'Hmmmmm...'
The Universe

*1 out of 10 dreamers dreamed big enough to
begin with. Whooooohoooooooooooooooooo!*

DREAM EVEN BIGGER

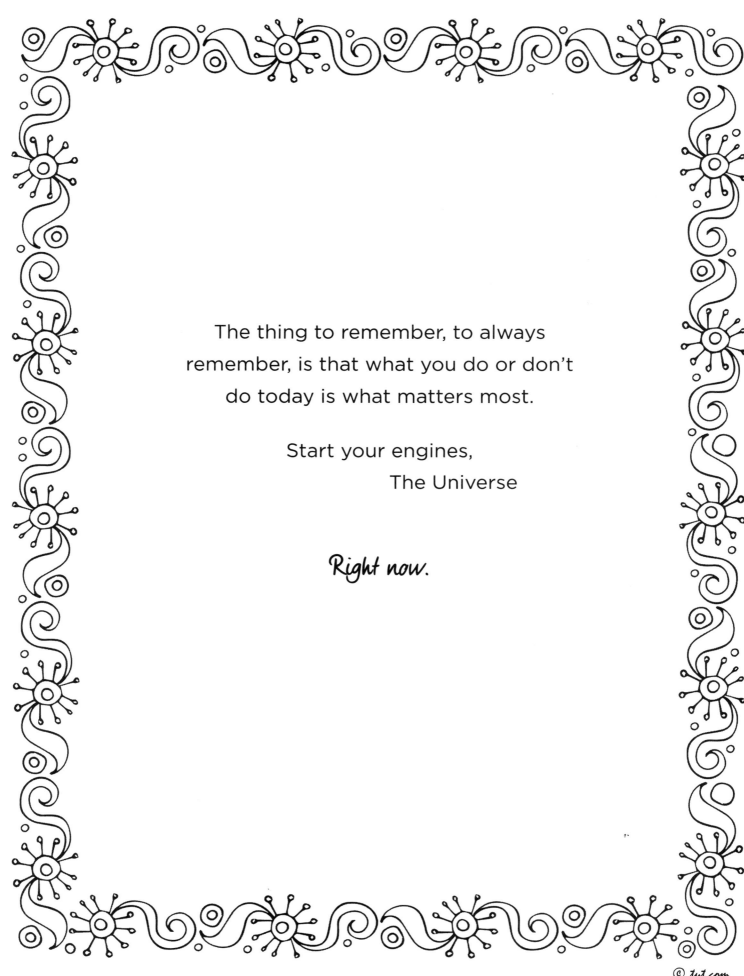

The thing to remember, to always remember, is that what you do or don't do today is what matters most.

Start your engines,
  The Universe

Right now.

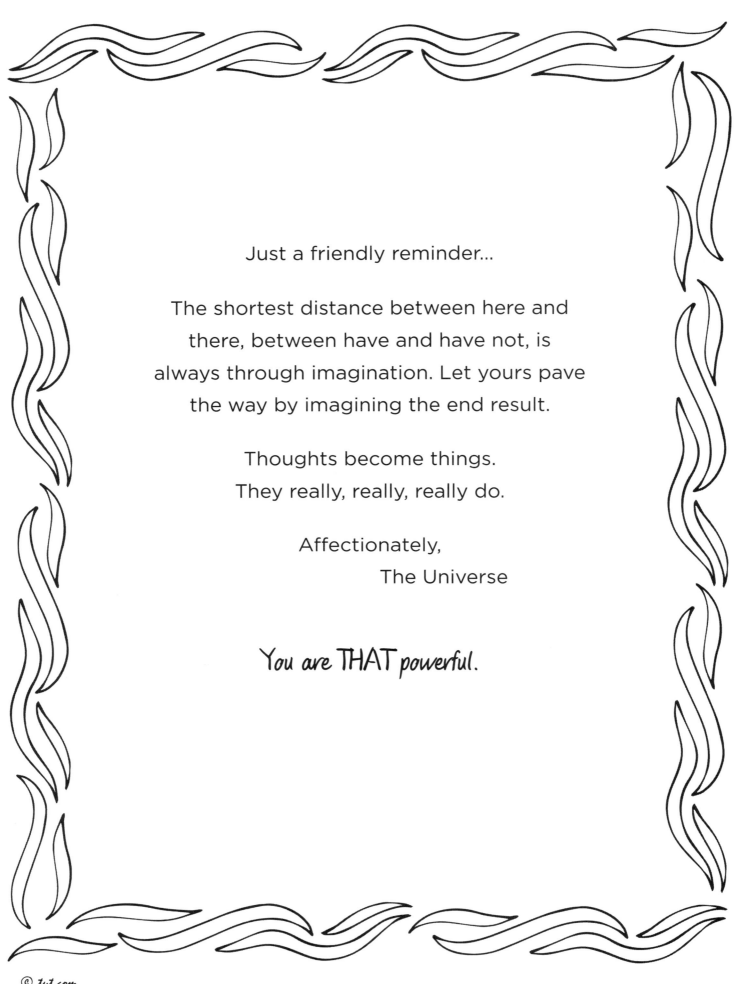

Just a friendly reminder...

The shortest distance between here and
there, between have and have not, is
always through imagination. Let yours pave
the way by imagining the end result.

Thoughts become things.
They really, really, really do.

Affectionately,
The Universe

You are THAT powerful.

Any and all forms of separation,
disconnects, divides, partings, break-ups
and goodbyes are temporary. Very.

You'll be together far, far longer
than you will ever be apart.

Forever and ever,
    The Universe

Your oneness is pure truth;
your separation is pure fantasy.

It is understandably human nature
to see yourself as small.

Until you stop seeing yourself as just human.

Should be easy for you...
The Universe

You are pure energy:
infinite, inexhaustible and irresistible.

Did you know that you have so many fans in the unseen who love you so much, that you never dream alone, cry in vain or sleep without guardians protecting you?

No matter how things may appear.

Cozy, cozy –

The Universe

Such is your effect on others. Including me.

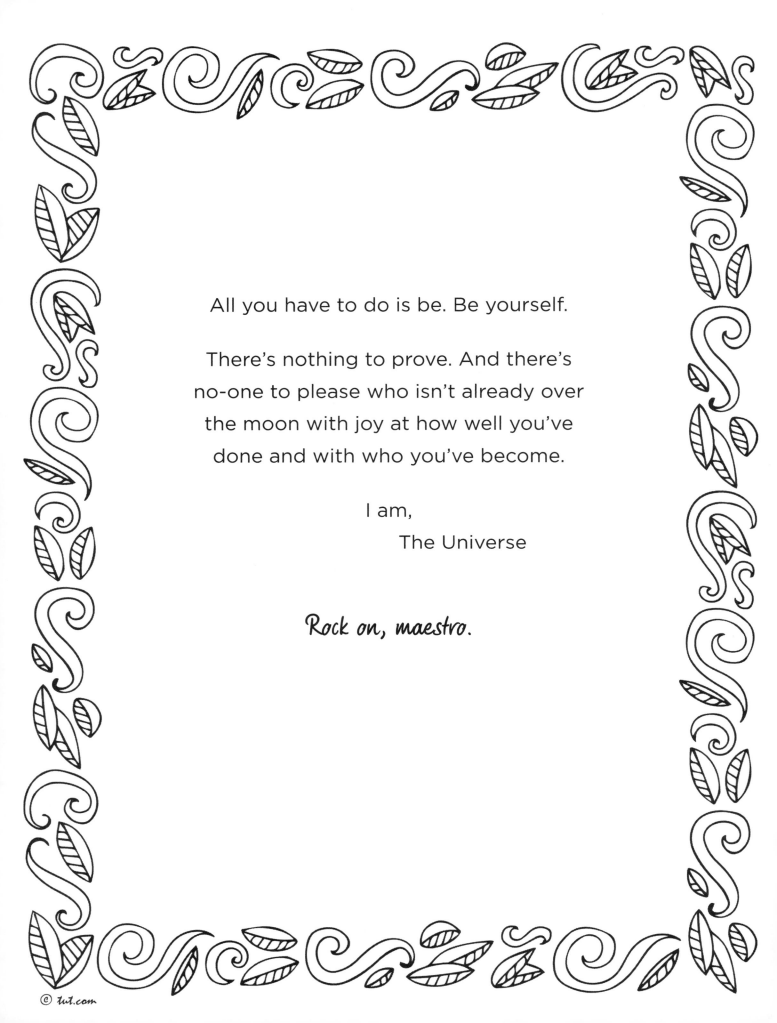

All you have to do is be. Be yourself.

There's nothing to prove. And there's no-one to please who isn't already over the moon with joy at how well you've done and with who you've become.

I am,

The Universe

Rock on, maestro.

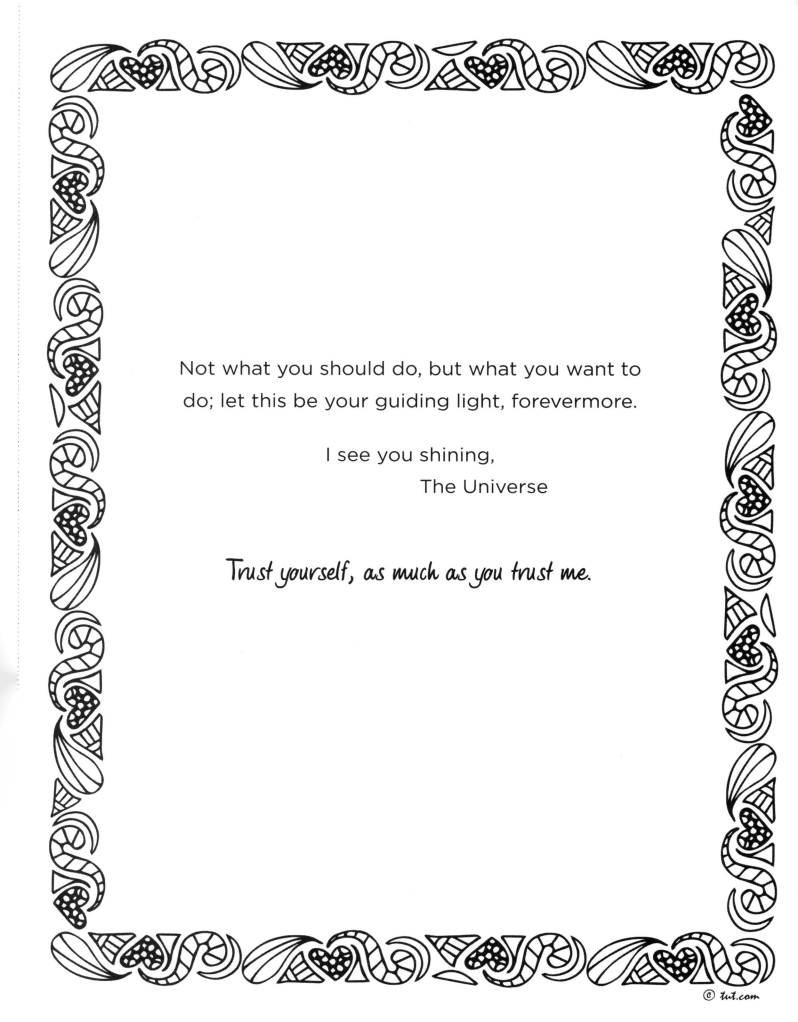

Not what you should do, but what you want to do; let this be your guiding light, forevermore.

I see you shining,

The Universe

Trust yourself, as much as you trust me.

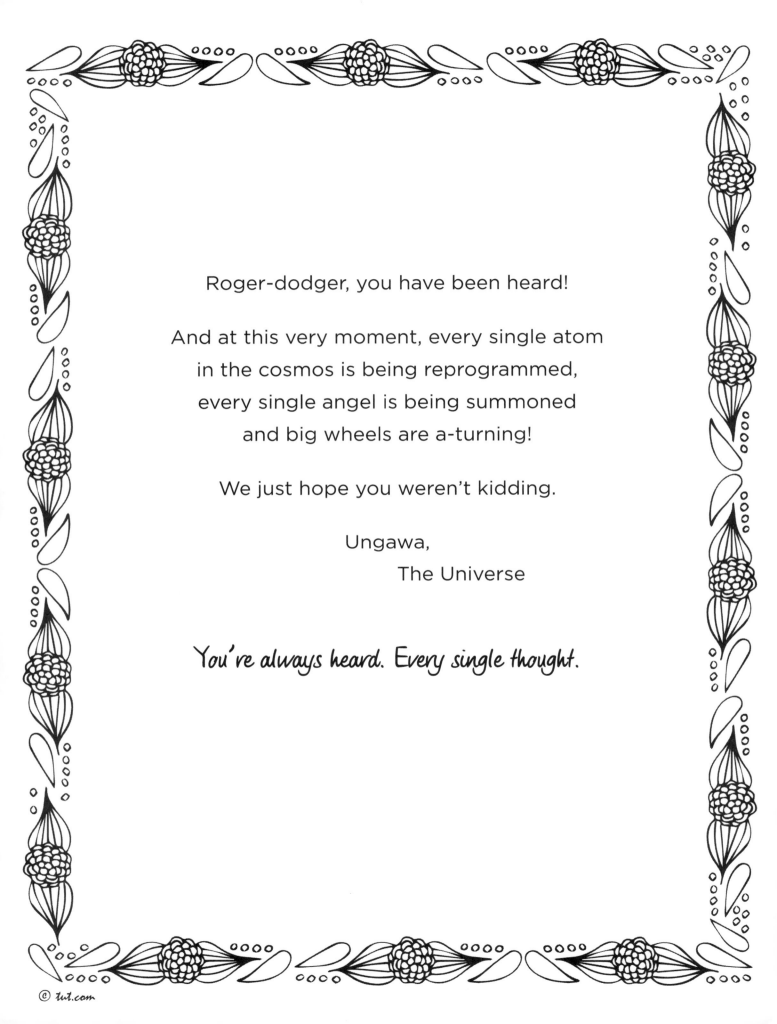

Roger-dodger, you have been heard!

And at this very moment, every single atom
in the cosmos is being reprogrammed,
every single angel is being summoned
and big wheels are a-turning!

We just hope you weren't kidding.

Ungawa,
    The Universe

You've always heard. Every single thought.

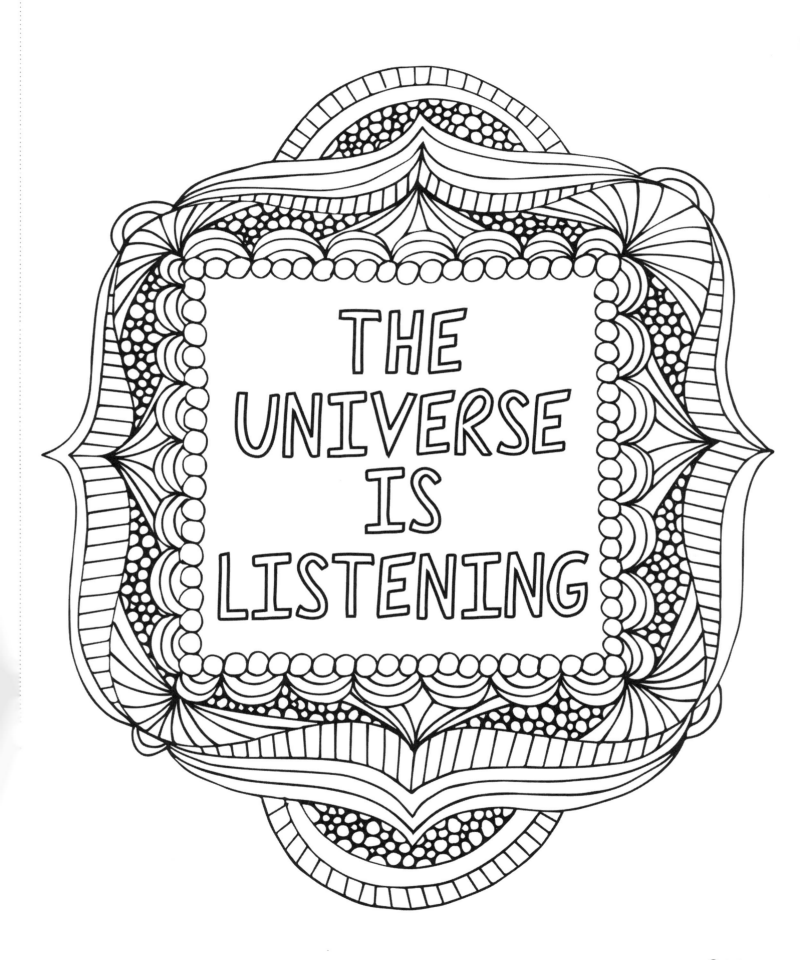

DREAM, BELIEVE, SHOW UP.

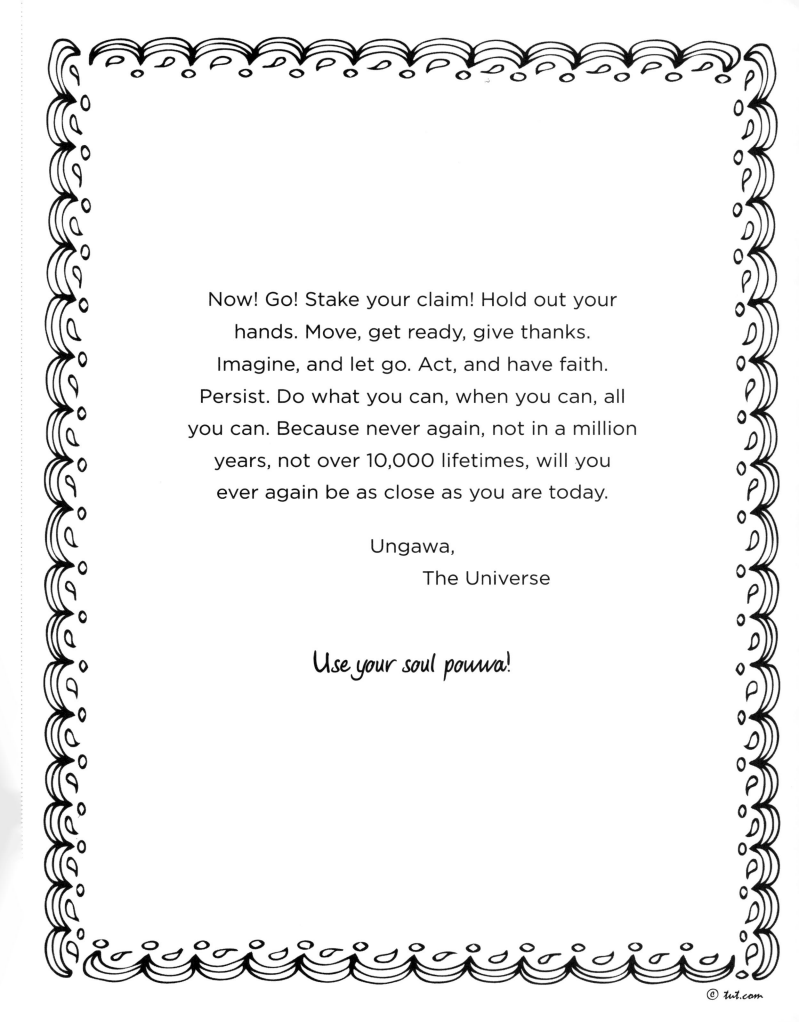

Now! Go! Stake your claim! Hold out your hands. Move, get ready, give thanks. Imagine, and let go. Act, and have faith. Persist. Do what you can, when you can, all you can. Because never again, not in a million years, not over 10,000 lifetimes, will you ever again be as close as you are today.

Ungawa,
     The Universe

Use your soul powwa!

Daily, hour by hour, minute by minute, second by second, you are admired by eyes in the unseen.

You are deeply understood. Your actions and inactions are honoured. Your thoughts and deeds are saluted. Even your fears and challenges are admired, along with the courage it took to choose them. (Yeah, you chose them.)

Having a connection with a soul as adventurous as yours gives all of us here reason to party like 'the roof is on fire.' Even though we usually don't have roofs.

Thanks from this side of the curtains,
The Universe

Lift your hands up and shout! Everybody now, shout! You're huge in the unseen!

© tut.com

U ♥ R LOVED

For the record, here's what really matters, every single day:

That you know how much you're loved.

Mean it,
    The Universe

Oh sure, tree hugging is up there, too, but it's not the same.

The thing about success is that she often arrives at such a late hour that only the oddballs, freaks and nuts (you know, the ones who continued believing in spite of all worldly evidence to the contrary) remain to greet her.

A little weird is good,
The Universe

Well, she doesn't have to arrive so late, but sometimes that's how long it takes before people stop fretting about whether or not she ever will.

© tut.com

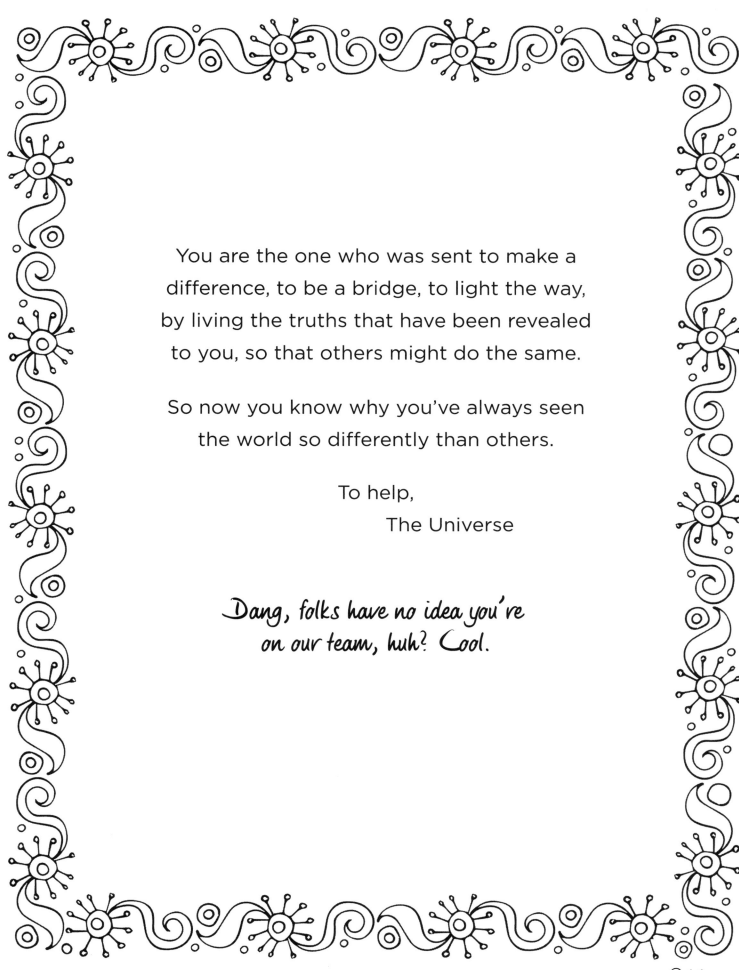

You are the one who was sent to make a difference, to be a bridge, to light the way, by living the truths that have been revealed to you, so that others might do the same.

So now you know why you've always seen the world so differently than others.

To help,
    The Universe

Dang, folks have no idea you're on our team, huh? Cool.

Do you know what 'unlimited' means?

It means you decide – everything.

Whoa,
    The Universe

Dang! You've got it made.

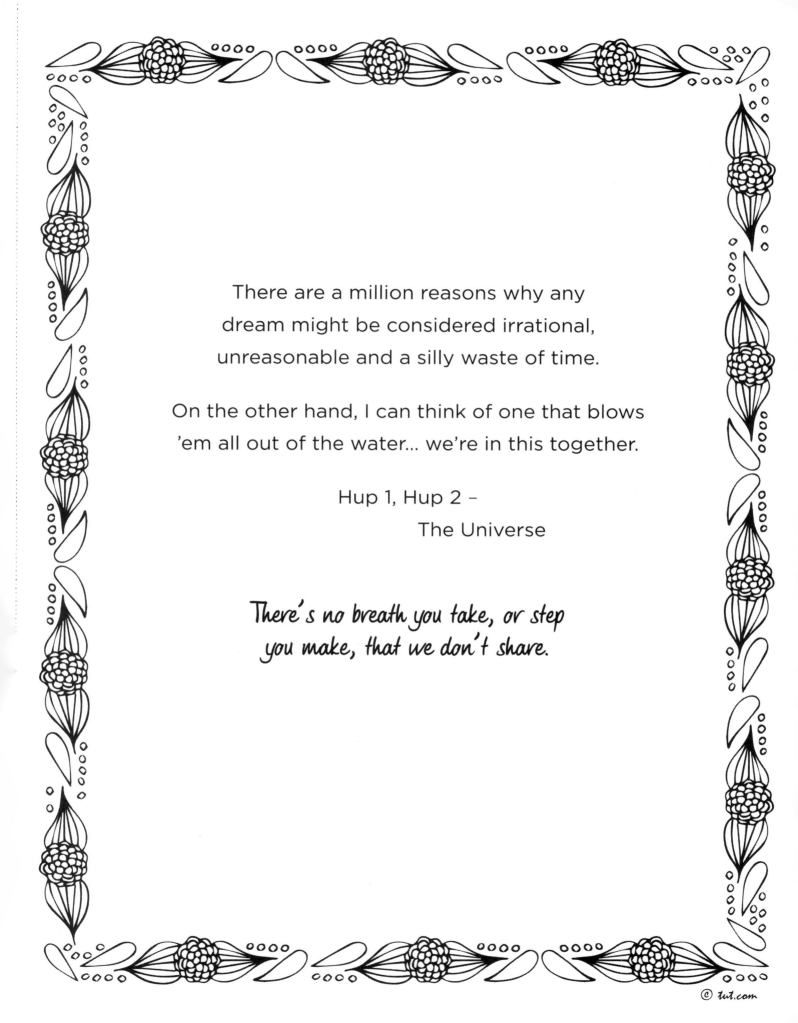

There are a million reasons why any
dream might be considered irrational,
unreasonable and a silly waste of time.

On the other hand, I can think of one that blows
'em all out of the water... we're in this together.

Hup 1, Hup 2 –

The Universe

There's no breath you take, or step
you make, that we don't share.

Relax. Breathe in deep. Hold it. Let it out. Loosen your shoulders. Smile. Close your eyes. And you'll be surprised at how many voices you'll hear, whispering sweet encouragement into your ear.

Kissey, kissey, you can do it –
The Universe

Be still, be calm and listen. You'll find there's nowhere you can't go, no challenge you can't master and no reason whatsoever that you can't have it all.

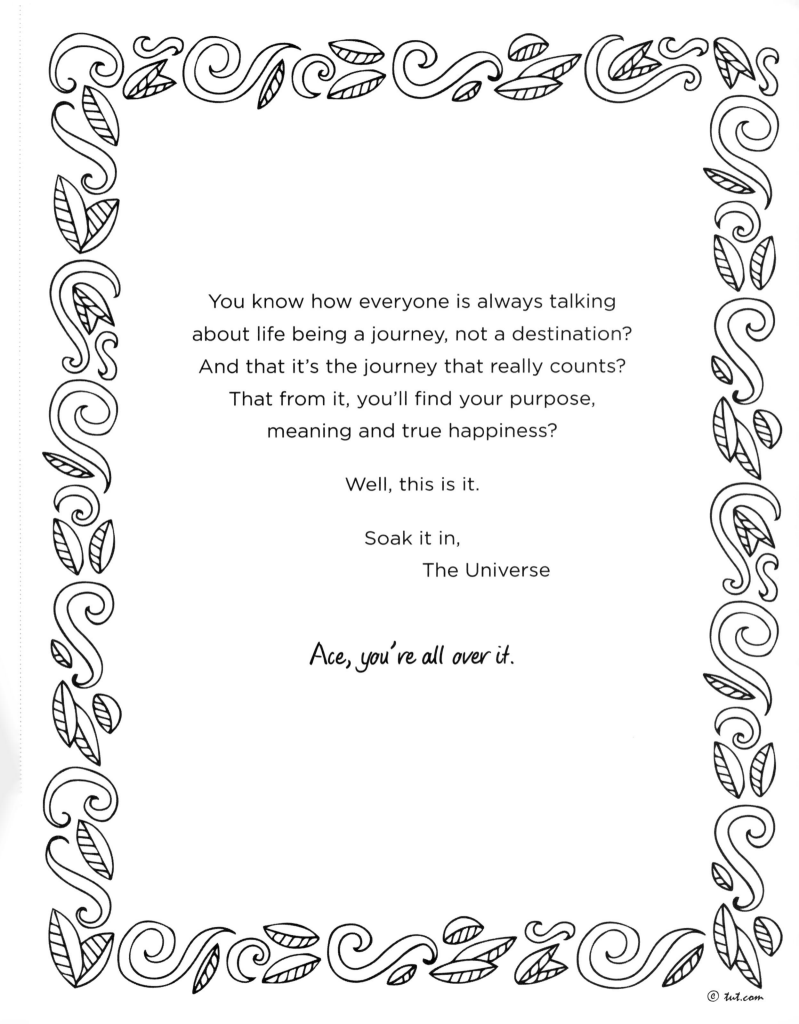

You know how everyone is always talking
about life being a journey, not a destination?
And that it's the journey that really counts?
That from it, you'll find your purpose,
meaning and true happiness?

Well, this is it.

Soak it in,
        The Universe

Ace, you're all over it.

Of course you don't have to visualize!!

Nor do you have to wear matching clothes,
chew food with your mouth closed,
sleep enough each night, brush your teeth,
bathe regularly, speak in complete sentences,
use proper grammar, run spellcheck,
zip up your fly or pay your bills on time.

But really, wouldn't you be mortified
if anyone found out?

I know I would...
The Universe

Now, if you were going to do just one of
those things every single day... Visualize.

VISUALIZE!

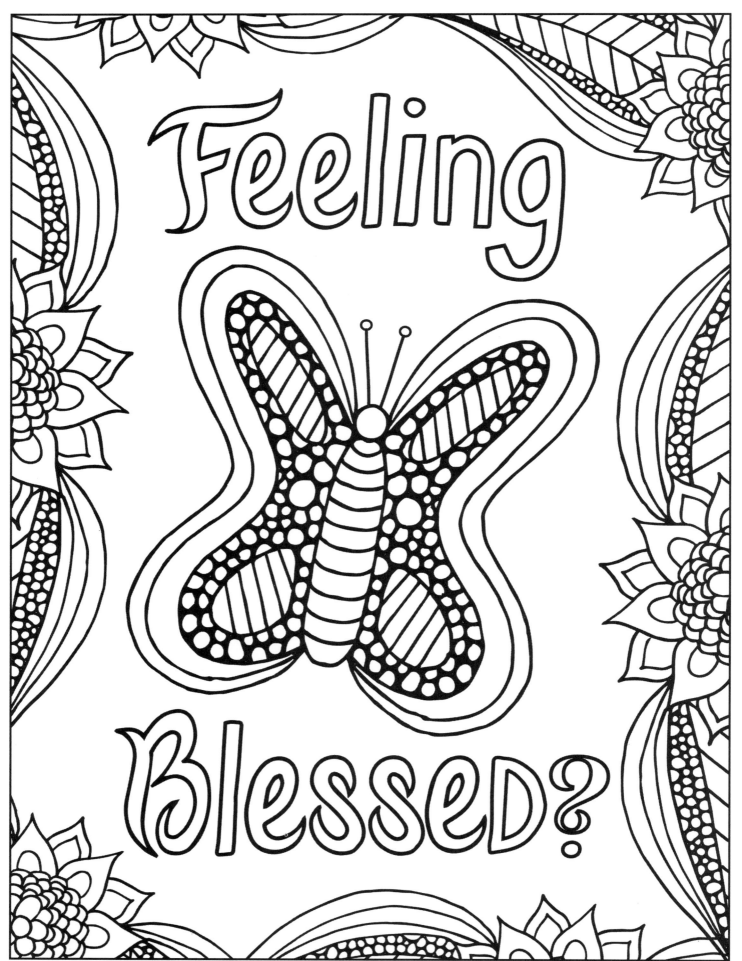

To find out how much you've truly been
blessed with in terms of love, time,
energy, talent, joy, abundance, confidence,
intelligence, wit or any other quality,
substance or dispensation, give of them.

Then you'll know what boundless really means.

Tallyho,
The Universe

*Just a little at first, then, as floodgates
swing open and chalices overflow, let's
give them something to talk about...*

Somewhere, over the rainbow, there's a world where birds sing into every night, flowers bloom across every land, each problem has 10,000 solutions and people live lives only to love and be loved...

Just like under the rainbow.

Ain't life grand?
The Universe

I can't begin to tell you how happy we've always been with your choice of Earth.

Be led by joy.

It's the whole point.

Tallyho,
    The Universe

Remember, before this entire adventure began, you once asked me to remind you of this? You asked that I time it right before the floodgates opened, so that you could stay grounded. You were studying at the prestigious Bent Light University... in the PhD programme... on a hula-hoop scholarship. 'Go Illuminators!'

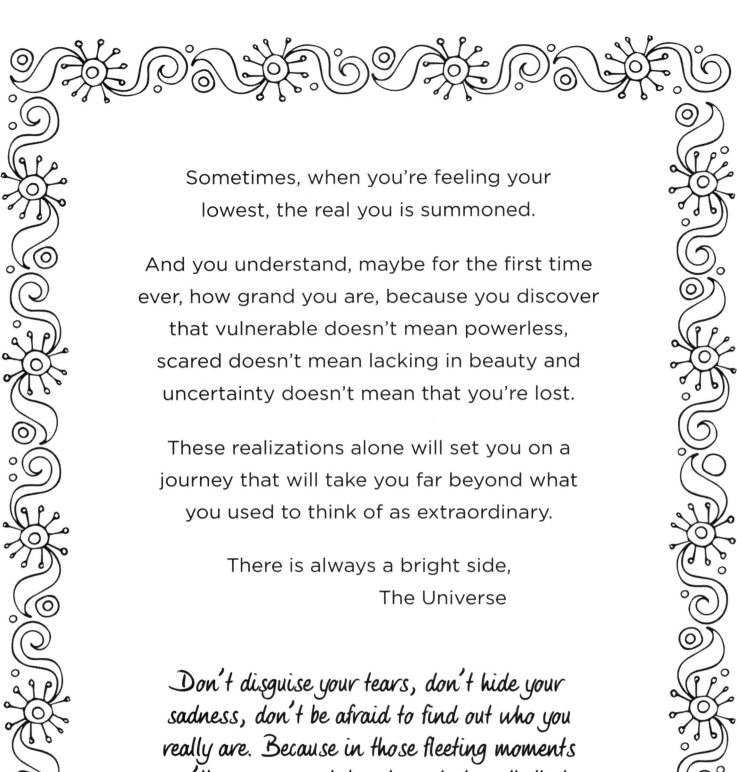

Sometimes, when you're feeling your lowest, the real you is summoned.

And you understand, maybe for the first time ever, how grand you are, because you discover that vulnerable doesn't mean powerless, scared doesn't mean lacking in beauty and uncertainty doesn't mean that you're lost.

These realizations alone will set you on a journey that will take you far beyond what you used to think of as extraordinary.

There is always a bright side,
The Universe

Don't disguise your tears, don't hide your sadness, don't be afraid to find out who you really are. Because in those fleeting moments you'll summon such beauty and strength that, in no time at all, you'll fully grasp exactly why you're so gossiped about here in the unseen.

THERE IS ALWAYS A BRIGHT SIDE

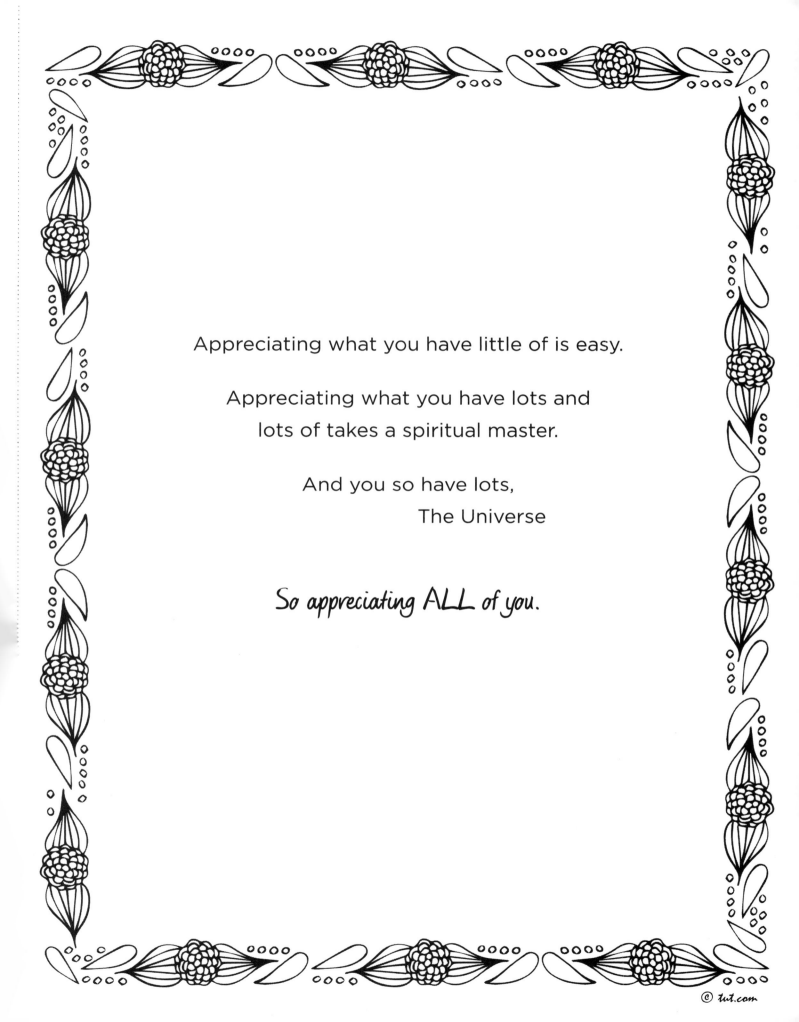

Appreciating what you have little of is easy.

Appreciating what you have lots and
lots of takes a spiritual master.

And you so have lots,
The Universe

So appreciating ALL of you.

This year will not be just another year.

It's the absolute richest I've ever imagined,
with the most possibilities I've ever offered,
for the coolest people I've ever known
to do the greatest things ever done.

Set the bar high,

The Universe

This year is yours, baby.

When you love who you are, you
become much more lovable.

Not that that's why I love you.

Love you,
    The Universe

I love you, for no reason.
Not that there aren't millions.
Now, after three mind-expanding
tangents, please reread the first line.

Some angels choose cleverly disguised
lives in time and space, just to help folks
get past judging by appearances.

No, they're not much to look at, listen to or
dance with, and most would never guess
they're angels... but that's the point.

Every soul is beautiful,
                        The Universe

Some even come as rappers, late night
radio personalities or billionaires!

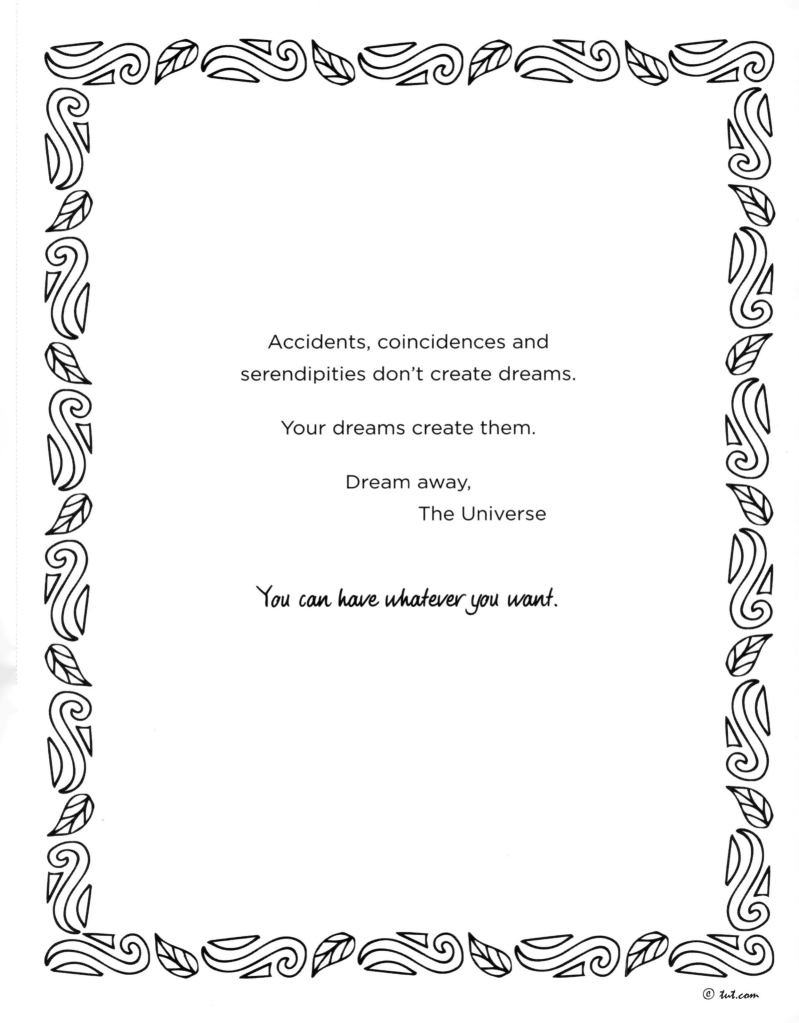

Accidents, coincidences and
serendipities don't create dreams.

Your dreams create them.

Dream away,
The Universe

You can have whatever you want.

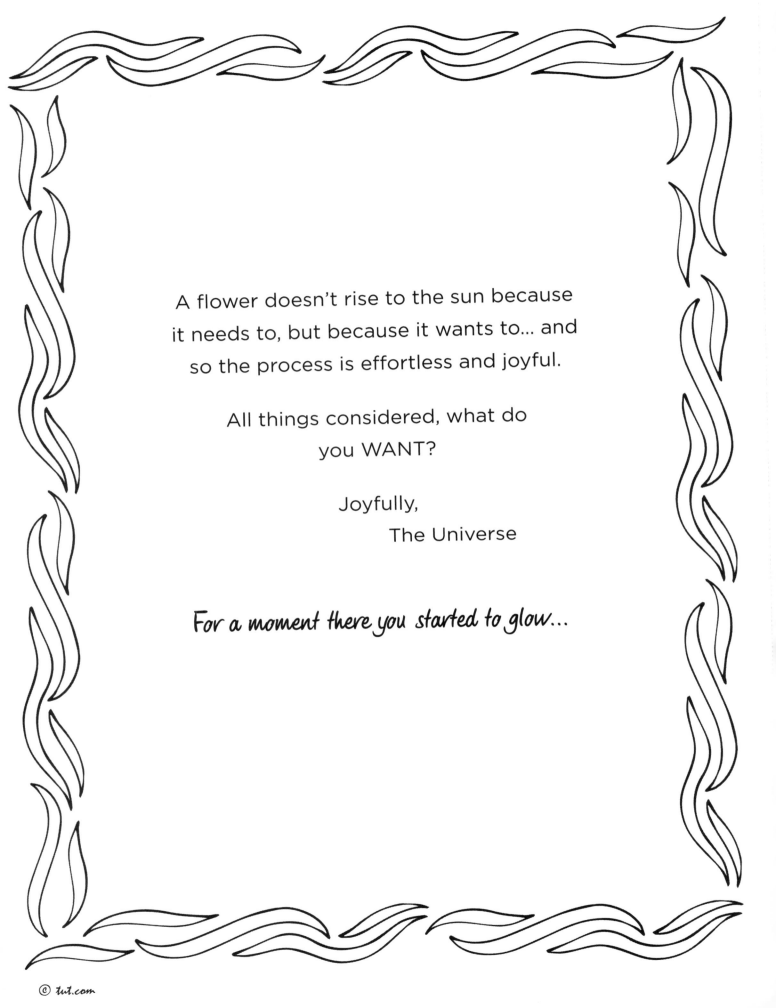

A flower doesn't rise to the sun because
it needs to, but because it wants to... and
so the process is effortless and joyful.

All things considered, what do
you WANT?

Joyfully,
The Universe

For a moment there you started to glow...

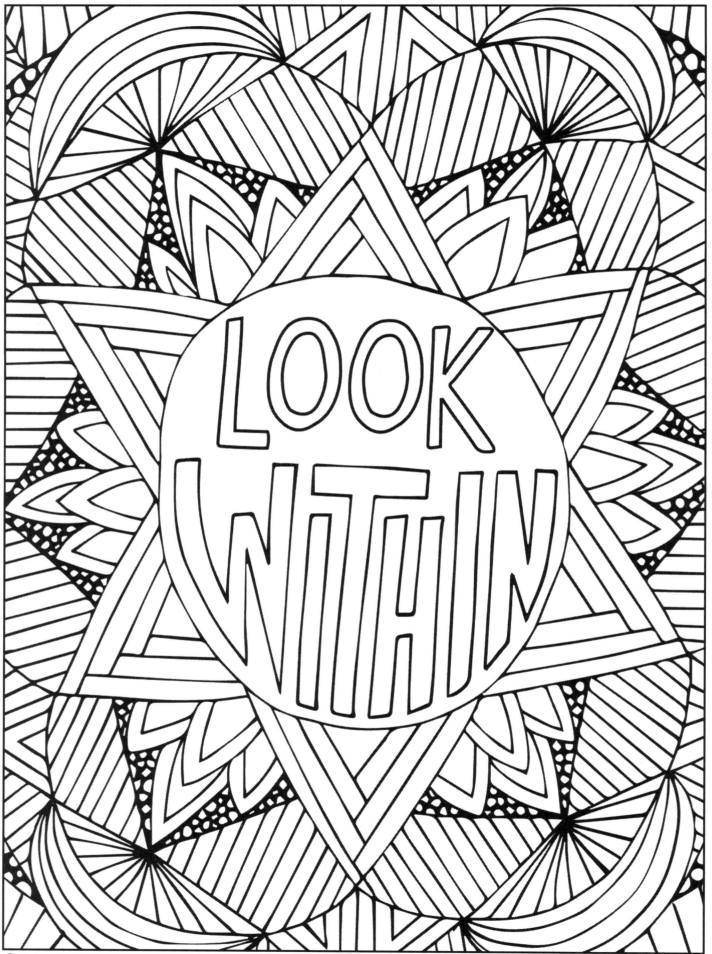

Ever notice that in the long run those who
don't eventually go 'within' often go 'without'?

You've got the power,
The Universe

That's where all the answers lie.

Happiness always returns.

You know, in case you should
ever sense its absence.

Tallyho,
    The Universe

Partly, because while it's away, it misses
you even more than you miss it.

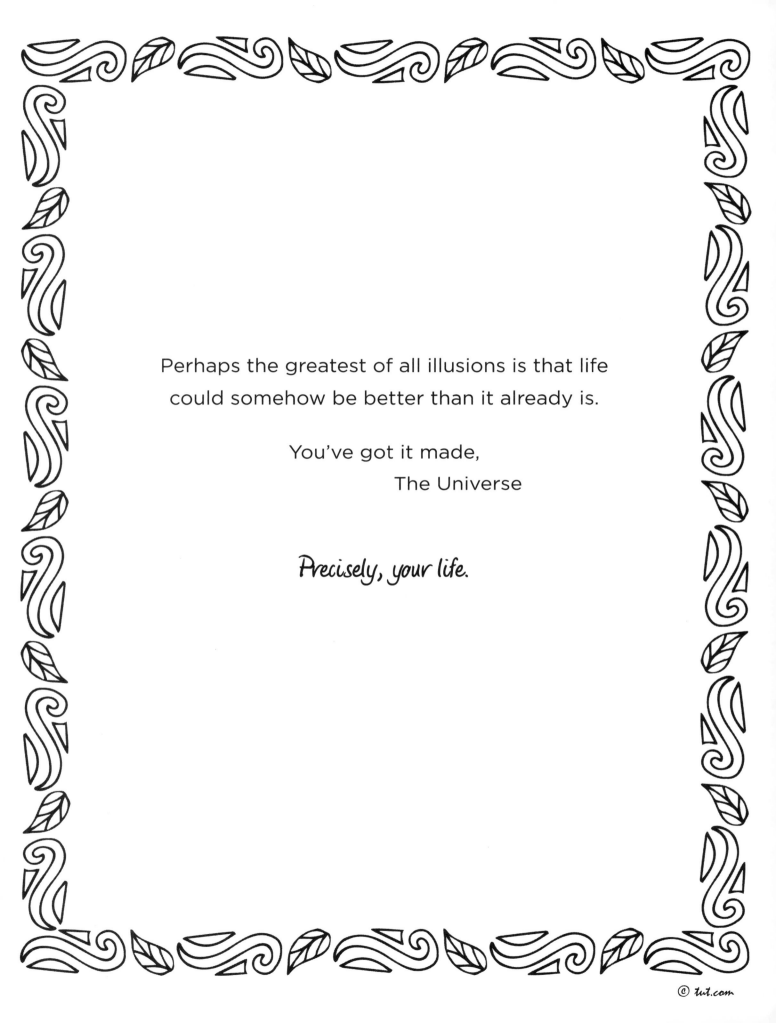

Perhaps the greatest of all illusions is that life could somehow be better than it already is.

You've got it made,
  The Universe

Precisely, your life.

You just never know who in the crowd, standing beside you in line or passing you in the street, might be raised in spirit, or even lifted from despair, by the kindness in your glance or the comfort of your smile.

But they may never forget.

Supersize me,
   The Universe

It takes so little.

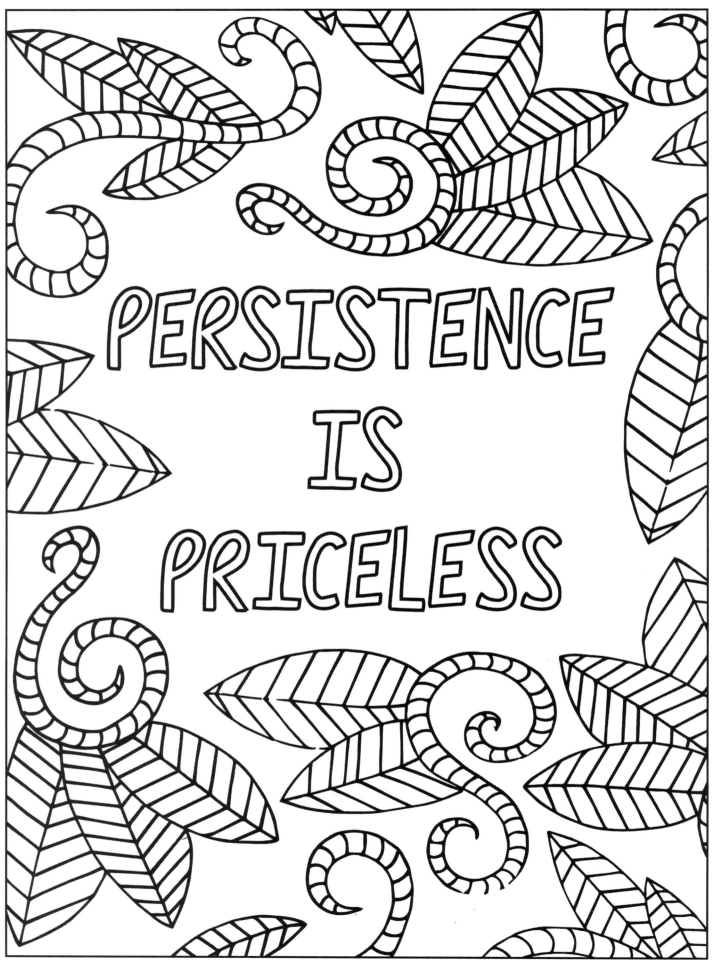

PERSISTENCE IS PRICELESS

Persistence is priceless, but its value
lies in doing, doing, doing; not in
waiting, waiting, waiting.

OK? OK? OK?
The Universe

*Not that you were hanging around for
someone, someway or somehow.*

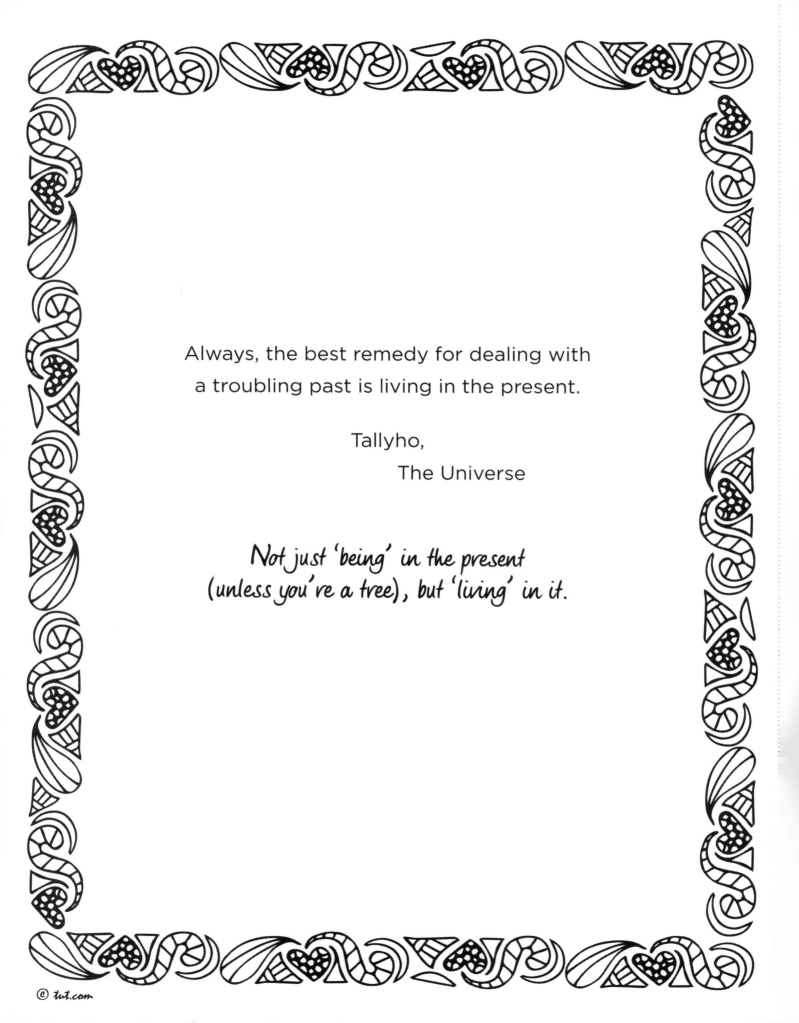

Always, the best remedy for dealing with
a troubling past is living in the present.

Tallyho,

The Universe

Not just 'being' in the present
(unless you're a tree), but 'living' in it.

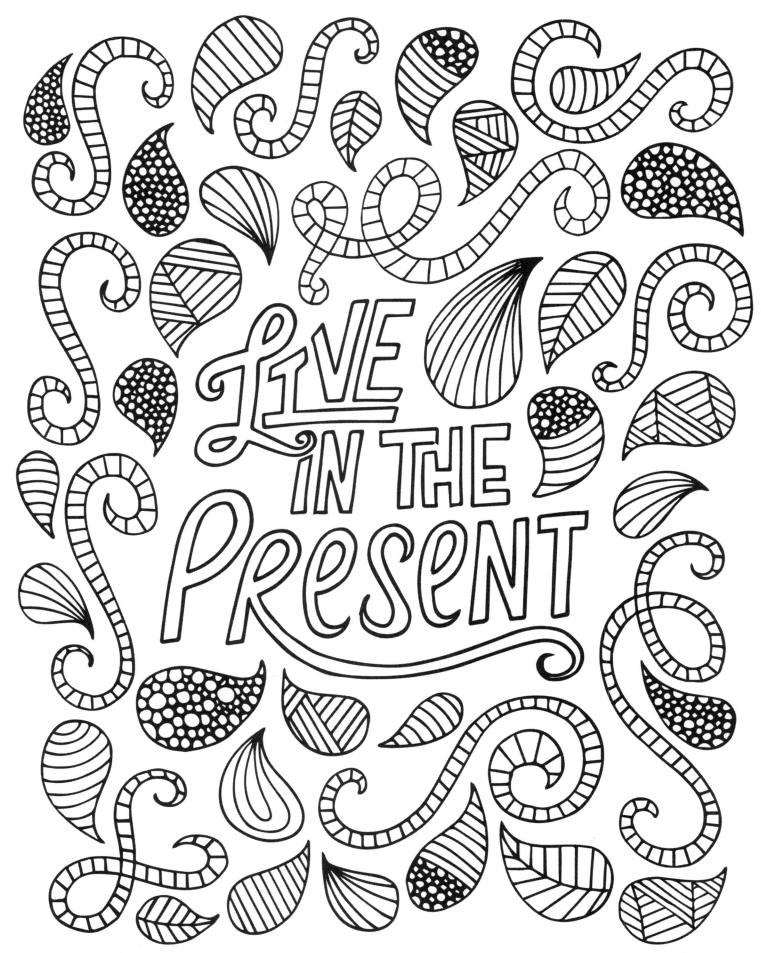

OK. OK. I confess.

No matter what you're after in life, getting what you want always boils down to at least a little bit of divine intervention.

But then, I'm talking about yours, not mine.

Bada-boom,
The Universe

You've got the power.

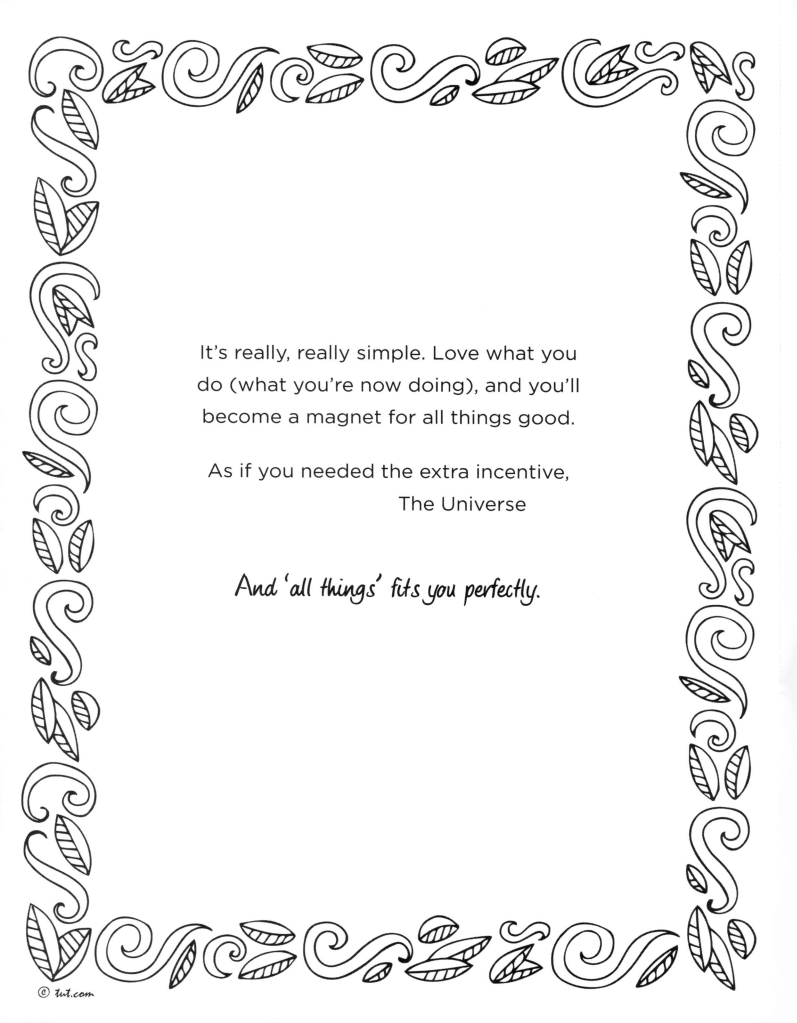

It's really, really simple. Love what you do (what you're now doing), and you'll become a magnet for all things good.

As if you needed the extra incentive,
The Universe

And 'all things' fits you perfectly.

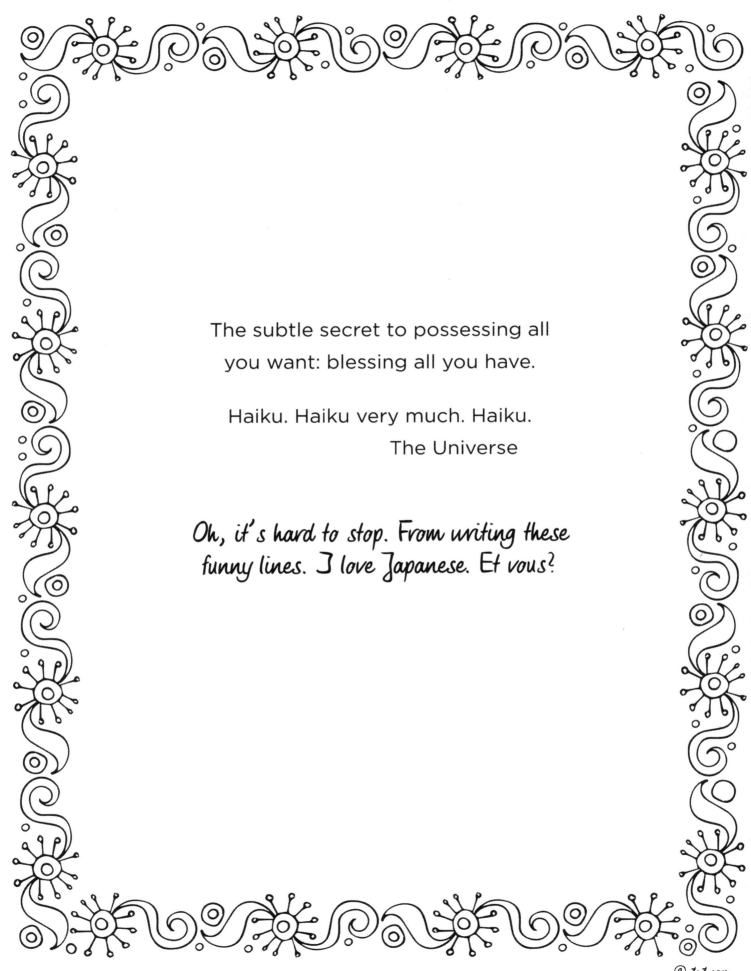

The subtle secret to possessing all
you want: blessing all you have.

Haiku. Haiku very much. Haiku.

The Universe

Oh, it's hard to stop. From writing these
funny lines. I love Japanese. Et vous?

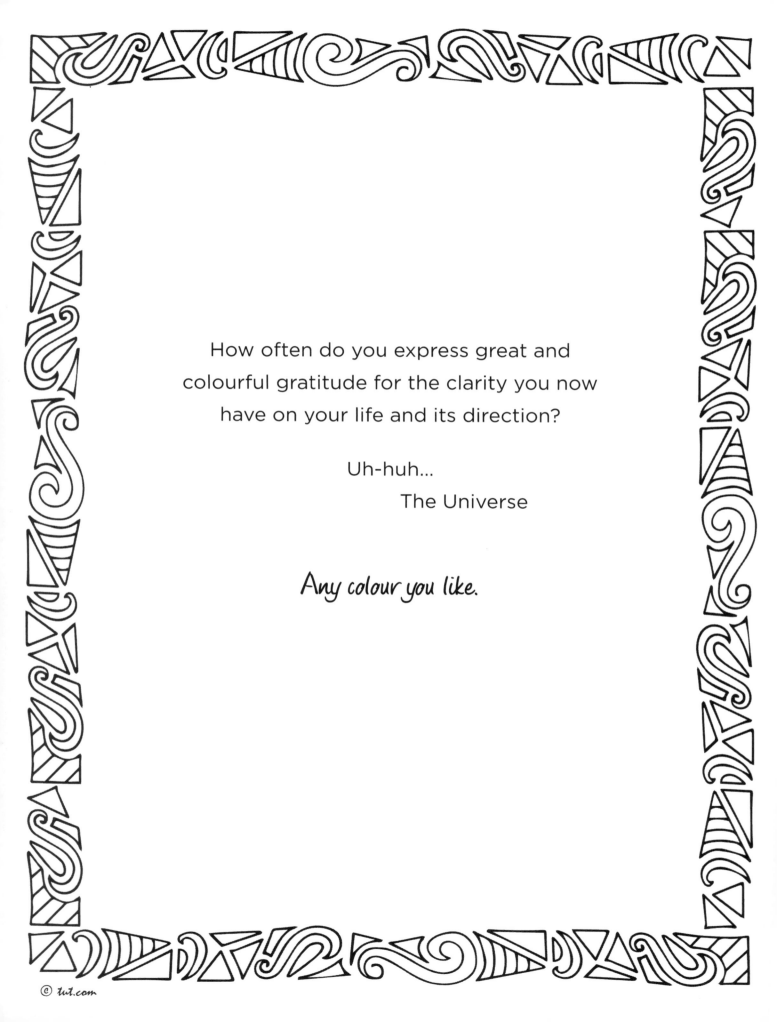

How often do you express great and
colourful gratitude for the clarity you now
have on your life and its direction?

Uh-huh...
The Universe

Any colour you like.

© tut.com